I Love to Watch You Play

a journey through little league baseball

Written by Beanie Hazelton

Illustrated by Tara J. Hannon

To Jacks,
Let's Go Mets!
Best wishes,
Beanie
Hazelton
8/10, 2019

Library of Congress Cataloging-in-Publication Data

I Love to Watch You Play
Beanie Hazelton
Cover Design and Illustrations by Tara J. Hannon
p.   cm.
ISBN: 978-0-943401-53-6
Library of Congress Control Number: 2018967573
A19
10 9 8 7 6 5 4 3 2 1
First Edition
Printed and Bound in the United States of America

A publication of TriMark Press, Inc.
368 South Military Trail
Deerfield Beach, FL 33442
800.889.0693
www.TriMarkPress.com

For Michael

The games are long, but the years are short.

-BH

Sell your books at sellbackyourBook.com! Go to sellbackyourBook.com and get an instant price quote. We even pay the shipping - see what your old books are worth today!

00043243708

0004324 **3708** S

DON'T LOOK
for any preaching between
the covers of this book. No lessons to be
learned. No advice. No moral of the story.
I present you with the simple and raw
utterances from parents who have sat
side by side with me in the rain, fog,
wind, sleet, and heat of summer....
soaking in the ups and downs of
life from the bleachers.

Opening Day brings high hopes for the new baseball season ahead.

Nothing is better than being together on a Sunday afternoon at the grand ballpark.

And acceptance is the rule.

Play ball. O ooo. Time. Safe. Looked good to me.
What?! Good call BLUE. Are you okay BLUE?
Forget your glasses? Not giving outside calls today?
Expand that a bit. Oh man, it was right down the
middle. Balk, balk, balk. Yerrr out!

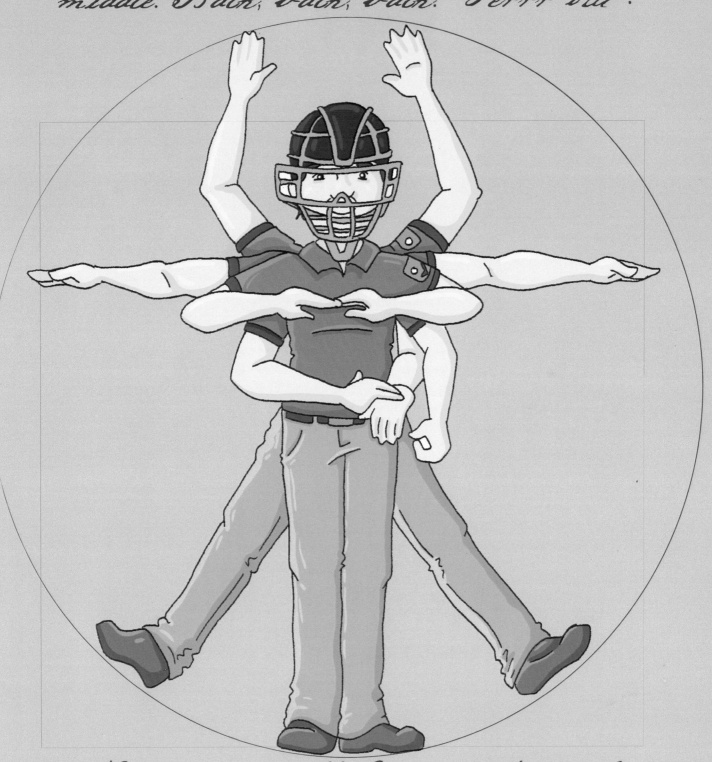

That was a ball. C'mon that's foul.
That's a warning. Where was that pitch BLUE?
Sweep the plate. What's the rule there?
You're missing a good ballgame here BLUE!

Yet there is triumph in mastery.

PLAY THE GLOVE · GOOD IDEA · YOU GOT THIS GUY

JUST THROW STRIKES · NO WORRIES · YOU'RE IN CHARGE

HIT YOUR SPOT · DOWN THE ALLEY · POWER T · 123.

DON'T LOSE HIM · PRETTY PITCH · NICE IDEA · STAY STRONG

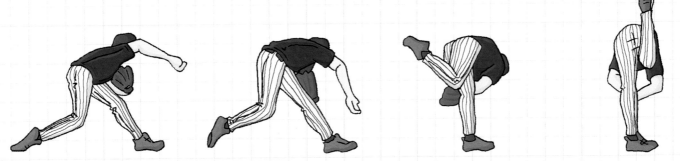

LET HIM HIT IT · WORK HARD · MAKE IT OFFICIAL

As we cheer the crunch of happy feet.

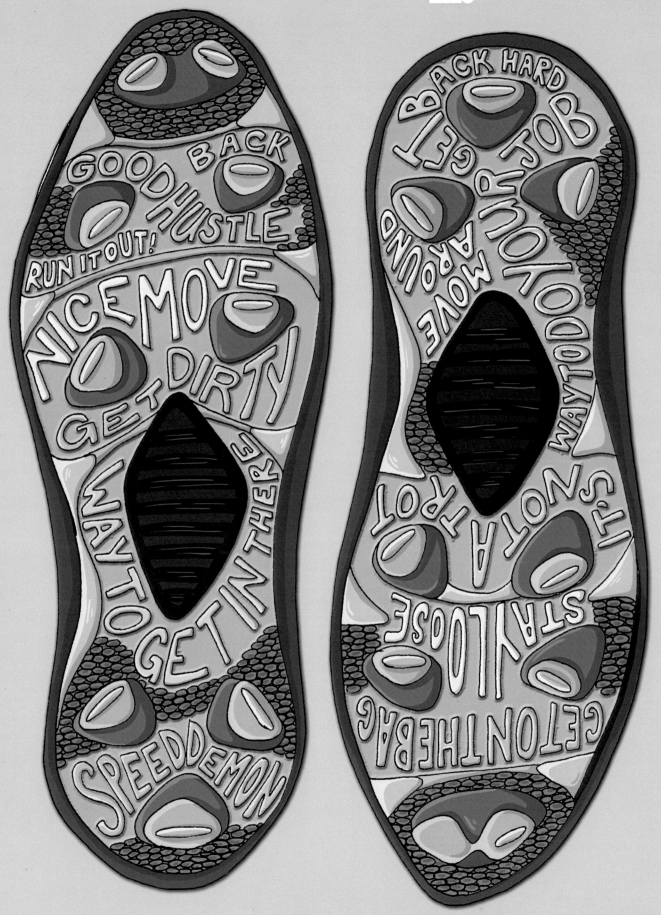

Each forward step and retreat unfolds before us.

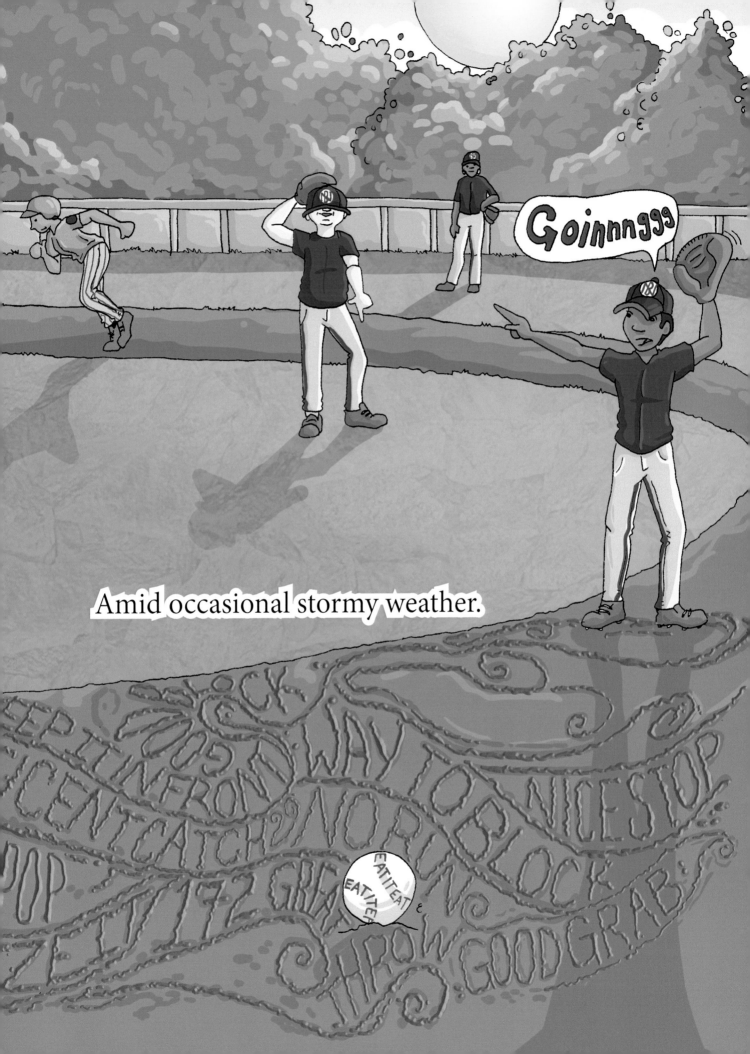

Amid occasional stormy weather.

We rise to our feet to do the Wave!

Our words celebrate our faith in you.

Six little words end a perfect day!

Beanie has been sitting on the bleachers for 25 years. She dedicates this book to all the kids who are about to put on a baseball uniform for the first time. And to the parents - their first fans.

photo credit: Mark C. Whipple

Tara learned a lot about the heart of baseball throughout this project. She looks forward to putting in her time on the bleachers in the years to come.

www.tarajhannon.com

Author's Thanks

This book would not have been possible
without the love and support
of my family, friends, coaches
and bleacher mates.
My heartfelt appreciation
to them all.

A huge thank you
to my illustrator Tara
for allowing me to dream big.
Our year-long collaboration was truly
Meant for a Moment.

Here's to the first fans!